THE ULT
OSTEOPOROSIS DIET COOKBOOK FOR WOMEN

Delicious and Nutrient-Rich Science Based and Calcium Fortified Recipes for Women with Osteoporosis

Dr. Mary D. Cook

OTHER BOOKS BY THE AUTHOR

1. OSTEOPOROSIS DIET COOKBOOK FOR SENIORS

CLICK HERE TO GET YOUR COPY NOW!!!

2. THE ULTIMATE GASTRIC SLEEVE BARIATRIC COOKBOOK

CLICK HERE TO GET YOUR COPY!!!

3. PESCATARIAN DIET COOKBOOK FOR DIABETICS

CLICK HER TO GET YOUR COPY NOW!!!

TABLE OF CONTENTS

INTRODUCTION

Welcome to an extraordinary journey towards robust bone health and vibrant well-being! I am Dr. Mary D. Cook, a seasoned nutritionist deeply committed to empowering women on their path to optimal health. Through my extensive experience, I have witnessed the profound impact of nutrition in combating osteoporosis and fostering enhanced bone vitality.

Osteoporosis, often underestimated, demands our focused attention. It's not merely about bones; it's about cultivating resilience, activity, and a life filled with fulfillment. This cookbook transcends the realm of recipes; it is a tailored guide addressing the distinctive nutritional needs of women navigating the challenges of osteoporosis.

Let me illuminate this journey through the inspiring narrative of Sarah, a dynamic woman in her mid-fifties who, like many others, found herself grappling with the complexities of osteoporosis. Sarah's diagnosis served as a pivotal moment, prompting her to seek guidance on navigating the intricate path towards bone health.

Together, we embarked on a culinary odyssey, exploring nutrient-dense foods and flavors that not only tantalized the palate but also emerged as formidable allies in her battle against osteoporosis.

We meticulously crafted a personalized dietary plan, spotlighting ingredients rich in calcium, vitamin D, and other essential nutrients crucial for bone strength.

As Sarah embraced this new approach to nourishing her body, the transformation was unmistakable. Over time, not only did her bone density stabilize, but signs of improvement began to manifest. Sarah's story stands as a beacon of hope, illustrating the profound impact the right diet can have on our health and well-being.

Within the pages of the "Osteoporosis Diet Cookbook for Women," you will uncover more than a compilation of recipes. Each dish is purposefully crafted: to nurture your bones, invigorate your body, and delight your taste buds. From calcium-rich breakfasts to satisfying dinners and bone-nourishing snacks, this cookbook embodies a holistic approach to crafting meals that not only bolster bone health but also celebrate the joy of eating.

I firmly believe that a bone-healthy diet should never compromise on flavor. Hence, every recipe presented here is an exquisite blend of nutrition and culinary delight, designed to make your journey towards better bone health both enjoyable and sustainable.

This cookbook transcends the conventional; it is not merely a collection of recipes but a guide, a roadmap intended to assist women, much like Sarah, in reclaiming control over their bone health.

Each dish represents a stride towards fortifying your bones and embracing a life infused with vitality.

So, let us embark on this culinary adventure together. May food be your medicine, and may these pages be your compass to a life where your bones stand as resilient as your spirit. Here's to embracing wellness, one delectable bite at a time.

Yours in health,

{Dr. Mary D. Cook}

CHAPTER 1:

What is osteoporosis?:

Osteoporosis, a disorder that gradually weakens bones, is typically overlooked until fractures occur. Osteoporosis, derived from the Greek words "osteo" meaning bone and "porosis" meaning porous, is defined by low bone density and quality, rendering bones weak and prone to fractures. This quiet but devastating disease affects millions of people worldwide, primarily women, and knowing its complexities is critical for prevention and successful care.

Bones are dynamic structures that are continually remodeling and replacing old bone with new. Osteoporosis disturbs this balance, leading bones to lose density and strength. While bone density typically declines with age, osteoporosis speeds the process, increasing susceptibility.

Types of osteoporosis:

There are two forms of osteoporosis: primary and secondary.

1. Primary osteoporosis: The most frequent kind, which is related with age. Women, particularly those who have experienced menopause, are at a greater risk due to hormonal changes that decrease bone density. During menopause, the hormone estrogen, which is important for bone health, declines considerably.

2. Secondary Osteoporosis: Secondary osteoporosis can occur at any age and is caused by underlying medical problems or drugs. Rheumatoid arthritis, hormonal problems, and long-term use of corticosteroids can all cause bone loss.

Causes of osteoporosis:

Understanding the causes of osteoporosis is important for successful prevention and management.

1. Hormonal Changes: Postmenopausal women undergo a significant reduction in estrogen, a hormone essential for bone health.

Lower estrogen levels hasten bone loss, rendering women more prone to osteoporosis.

2. Age: Aging is a natural risk factor for osteoporosis. As people age, their bone density diminishes, and the pace of bone creation may not match the rate of bone loss.

3. Family History: Genetics influences bone health. Individuals with a family history of osteoporosis may be predisposed to the illness.

4. Lifestyle Factors: Sedentary lifestyles, a lack of weight-bearing activity, and poor diet can all lead to bone loss.

Smoking and heavy alcohol intake have also been related to increased risk.

5. Medical Conditions and Medications: Celiac disease and inflammatory illnesses can have an influence on bone health. Long-term usage of drugs such as corticosteroids may also result in bone loss.

Symptoms of osteoporosis:

Osteoporosis is known as the "silent disease" because it advances without obvious signs until a fracture occurs. However, there are minor indicators that might suggest its presence:

1. Back discomfort: Vertebral fractures can result in persistent back discomfort and a stooped posture.

2. Loss of Height: Compression fractures in the spine can cause progressive loss of height.

3. Fractures: Osteoporosis increases the risk of fractures, particularly those in the hip, spine, and wrist.

Preventive measures for osteoporosis:

Prevention is essential for controlling osteoporosis. Incorporating the following practices into everyday life can considerably lower the likelihood of getting the illness.

1. **Nutrient-Rich Diet:** Calcium and vitamin D are required for bone health. Dairy products, leafy greens, and fortified meals are all good sources.

2. **Regular Exercise:** Weight-bearing workouts like walking, running, and strength training promote bone growth and density.

3. **Adequate Sun Exposure:** Vitamin D, which is necessary for calcium absorption, is generated by the skin in reaction to sunshine. Ensure that you get 10-30 minutes of sunshine many times each week.

4. **Limiting Alcohol and Quitting Smoking:** Heavy drinking and smoking can damage bones. Limiting these practices promotes total bone health.

5. **Regular Bone Density Testing:** Regular bone density examinations can detect abnormalities early, allowing for prompt intervention, particularly in postmenopausal women and those at higher risk.

6. Healthier Lifestyle Options: Maintaining a healthy weight and controlling stress have a good influence on bone health. Chronic stress can cause the release of chemicals that promote bone loss.

7. Medication as needed: In rare circumstances, medication may be administered to decrease bone loss or increase bone production. It is critical to contact with a healthcare expert to identify the most appropriate treatment approach.

Osteoporosis is a powerful foe, but with understanding and proactive steps, its effects can be reduced. Understanding the condition, recognizing risk factors, and adopting a bone-healthy lifestyle are critical components of preventing osteoporosis and supporting long-term bone health.

Individuals may achieve strong, resilient bones that support a bright and active life by taking a comprehensive approach that includes nutrition, exercise, and regular medical check-ups.

CHAPTER 2:

The Benefits of an Osteoporosis Diet for Women:

A personalized osteoporosis diet is more than simply a collection of recipes; it is a potent approach for protecting women from the silent threat of bone loss. As women age, particularly after menopause, their risk of osteoporosis rises, emphasizing the significance of a proactive and nutrition-based strategy. Here, we look at the many benefits of an osteoporosis diet, demonstrating how wise food choices may form a foundation for bone health.

1. Optimal Nutritional Intake: An osteoporosis diet promotes elements essential for bone health. Calcium, the major mineral in bones, serves as the foundation of this method. Calcium-rich foods, such as dairy products, leafy greens, and fortified foodstuffs, provide an adequate consumption to promote bone density.

2. Vitamin D Synthesis: Vitamin D, sometimes known as the sunshine vitamin, promotes calcium absorption. An osteoporosis diet emphasizes vitamin D-rich foods such as fatty fish, eggs, and sunshine.

Adequate quantities of this vitamin help to maintain strong, durable bones.

3. Protein for Bone Structure: An osteoporosis diet should contain lean protein sources such as poultry, fish, legumes, and nuts to support bone structure. These proteins offer the amino acids required for bone formation and repair.

4. Magnesium and Other Micronutrients: Magnesium, together with vitamin K and phosphorus, promotes bone health. Nuts, seeds, whole grains, and green vegetables, commonly seen in an osteoporosis diet, give a diverse assortment of these essential nutrients.

5. Alkaline-Forming meals: Alkaline-forming meals assist balance the body's acidity and prevent mineral loss from bones. Fruits, vegetables, and legumes, which are essential components of an osteoporosis diet, help to create a more alkaline environment that promotes bone health.

6. Healthy Fats for Hormonal Balance: Essential fatty acids, especially omega-3s found in fatty fish and flaxseeds, are crucial for hormonal balance. Hormonal variations, particularly the drop in estrogen during menopause, are associated with bone loss. Including healthy fats in your diet helps improve hormonal balance.

7. Collagen-Rich Foods: Collagen is a protein that helps maintain bones.

An osteoporosis diet contains collagen-rich foods, such as bone broth, which may help to preserve bone integrity and strength.

8. Antioxidant Protection: Antioxidants help prevent chronic inflammation, which can lead to bone loss. Fruits and vegetables, which are plentiful in an osteoporosis diet, are high in antioxidants, providing protection from oxidative stress, which can harm bone health.

9. Weight Management: Keeping a healthy weight is essential for bone health. An osteoporosis diet promotes a balanced nutritional intake, aids in weight control, and lowers the danger of excess body weight, which can strain the skeletal system.

10. Hydration for Bone Density: Maintaining proper hydration is crucial for bone density and general health. Water is essential for the delivery of nutrients to bone cells, and an osteoporosis diet encourages hydration by consuming water-rich foods and drinks.

In summary, the advantages of an osteoporosis diet stretch well beyond the primary objective of avoiding bone loss. It takes a comprehensive approach to women's health, focusing on dietary needs, hormonal balance, and general well-being. Women who follow the principles of this particular diet can strengthen their bones, overcome the problems of osteoporosis, and begin on a path to a life of strength, energy, and long-term health.

Foods to Consider for Osteoporosis Prevention and Management:

1. **Dairy Products:** Low-fat or fat-free milk, yogurt, and cheese are great sources of calcium, which is crucial for bone health.

2. **Leafy Greens:** Kale, broccoli, spinach, and collard greens provide calcium, vitamin K, and other minerals that promote bone density.

3. **Fatty Fish:** Salmon, mackerel, and sardines provide vitamin D and omega-3 fatty acids, which promote calcium absorption and bone health.

4. **Fortified Foods:** Fortified cereals, orange juice, and plant-based milk replacements provide extra calcium and vitamin D.

5. **Lean Protein:** Consume lean protein sources such as poultry, fish, beans, lentils, and tofu to support bone health and regeneration.

6. **Nuts and Seeds:** Almonds, chia seeds, and flaxseeds include magnesium, phosphorus, and other nutrients needed for bone health.

7. **Fruits:** Citrus fruits, strawberries, and kiwi provide vitamin C, which promotes collagen and bone health.

8. Whole Grains: Quinoa, brown rice, and whole wheat products include magnesium and phosphorus, which are needed for bone formation.

9. Bone Broth: High in collagen, bone broth promotes connective tissue and may improve bone health.

10. Water: Include Staying hydrated is important for general health, including bone density.

Foods to Avoid in Osteoporosis Prevention and Management:

1. Limit Red Meat: Consuming too much red meat might lead to increased acidity and disrupt calcium balance.

2. Caffeine Limit: Excessive caffeine consumption may affect calcium absorption. Limit your intake of caffeine-containing drinks such as coffee and tea.

3. Limit salt intake, as high levels might lead to calcium loss. Limit processed meals, canned soups, and salty snacks.

4. Limit alcohol intake since it might significantly damage bone health. Moderation is essential to minimizing its effects.

5. Limit soda and sugary beverages due to phosphoric acid, which may interfere with calcium absorption. Choose water or calcium-fortified drinks.

6. Limit high-phosphorus foods, such as cola drinks and processed meats, as they might impact calcium balance.

CHAPTER 3:

Bone-Boosting breakfast recipes:

1. Berry Blast Protein Smoothie

Ingredients:

- 1/2 cup mixed berries (strawberries, blueberries, raspberries)
- 1/2 cup unsweetened almond milk
- 1/2 cup Greek yogurt (low-fat)
- 1 scoop vanilla protein powder
- Ice cubes (optional)

Preparation:

1. Blend berries, almond milk, Greek yogurt, and protein powder until smooth.
2. Add ice cubes if desired and blend again until well combined.
3. Pour into a glass and enjoy!

Servings: 1

Nutritional Value (approx.): Calories: 200, Protein: 25g, Carbohydrates: 15g, Fat: 5g, Fiber: 5g

Cooking Time: 5 minutes

2. Green Goddess Protein Smoothie

Ingredients:

- 1/2 cup spinach leaves
- 1/2 cucumber, peeled and sliced
- 1/2 avocado
- 1/2 cup unsweetened coconut water
- 1 scoop plant-based protein powder
- Mint leaves for garnish

Preparation:

1. Blend spinach, cucumber, avocado, coconut water, and protein powder until smooth.
2. Pour into a glass, garnish with mint leaves, and serve.

Servings: 1

Nutritional Value (approx.): Calories: 220, Protein: 20g, Carbohydrates: 12g, Fat: 10g, Fiber: 8g

Cooking Time: 5 minutes

3. Tropical Paradise Protein Smoothie

Ingredients:

- 1/2 cup pineapple chunks
- 1/2 banana
- 1/2 cup coconut milk (unsweetened)
- 1 scoop vanilla protein powder
- Ice cubes (optional)

Preparation:

1. Blend pineapple, banana, coconut milk, and protein powder until smooth.
2. Add ice cubes if desired and blend again until well combined.
3. Pour into a glass and transport yourself to a tropical paradise!

Servings: 1

Nutritional Value (approx.): Calories: 220, Protein: 22g, Carbohydrates: 20g, Fat: 7g, Fiber: 3g

Cooking Time: 5 minutes

4. Almond and Chia Seed Pudding

Ingredients:

- 2 tbsp chia seeds
- 1/2 cup unsweetened almond milk
- 1/4 cup sliced almonds
- 1/2 tsp vanilla extract
- Berries for topping

Preparation:

1. In a bowl, mix chia seeds, almond milk, sliced almonds, and vanilla extract.
2. Stir well and refrigerate overnight or for at least 4 hours.
3. Top with fresh berries before serving.

Servings: 1

Nutritional Value (approx.):

- Calories: 180
- Protein: 8g
- Carbohydrates: 15g
- Fat: 10g
- Fiber: 9g

Cooking Time: Overnight (or at least 4 hours)

5. Spinach and Feta Omelette Roll

Ingredients:

- 2 eggs
- 1/4 cup spinach, chopped
- 2 tbsp feta cheese, crumbled
- Salt and pepper to taste
- Fresh herbs for garnish

Preparation:

1. Whisk eggs in a bowl and season with salt and pepper.
2. Pour the egg mixture into a heated, non-stick pan.
3. Add chopped spinach and feta cheese on one side.
4. Roll the omelette and let it cook for an additional minute.
5. Garnish with fresh herbs before serving.

Servings: 1

Nutritional Value (approx.): Calories: 220, Protein: 18g, Carbohydrates: 2g, Fat: 16g, Fiber: 1g

Cooking Time: 5 minutes

6. Quinoa Breakfast Bowl

Ingredients:

- 1/2 cup cooked quinoa
- 1/4 cup sliced almonds
- 1/2 cup low-fat Greek yogurt
- 1/2 cup mixed berries
- Drizzle of honey

Preparation:

1. In a bowl, layer cooked quinoa, sliced almonds, Greek yogurt, and mixed berries.
2. Drizzle with honey before serving.

Servings: 1

Nutritional Value (approx.):

- Calories: 250
- Protein: 15g
- Carbohydrates: 30g
- Fat: 8g
- Fiber: 6g

Cooking Time: 10 minutes (if quinoa is not pre-cooked)

7. Yogurt Parfait with Nuts and Berries

Ingredients:

- 1/2 cup low-fat Greek yogurt
- 1/4 cup mixed nuts (almonds, walnuts)
- 1/2 cup mixed berries
- 1 tsp honey

Preparation:

1. In a glass, layer Greek yogurt, mixed nuts, and berries.
2. Repeat the layers.
3. Drizzle honey on top before serving.

Servings: 1

Nutritional Value (approx.):

- Calories: 250
- Protein: 15g
- Carbohydrates: 20g
- Fat: 12g
- Fiber: 5g

Preparation Time: 5 minutes

8. Salmon and Avocado Toast

Ingredients:

- 1 slice whole-grain bread
- 2 oz smoked salmon
- 1/4 avocado, sliced
- Fresh dill for garnish
- Lemon wedge

Preparation:

1. Toast the whole-grain bread.
2. Top with smoked salmon and sliced avocado.
3. Garnish with fresh dill and a squeeze of lemon.

Servings: 1

Nutritional Value (approx.):

- Calories: 280
- Protein: 20g
- Carbohydrates: 20g
- Fat: 15g
- Fiber: 6g

Cooking Time: 5 minutes

9. Cottage Cheese and Pineapple Bowl

Ingredients:

- 1/2 cup low-fat cottage cheese
- 1/2 cup fresh pineapple chunks
- 2 tbsp chopped mint leaves
- 1 tbsp sunflower seeds

Preparation:

1. In a bowl, combine cottage cheese and pineapple chunks.
2. Sprinkle chopped mint leaves and sunflower seeds on top.

Servings: 1

Nutritional Value (approx.):

- Calories: 200
- Protein: 15g
- Carbohydrates: 25g
- Fat: 5g
- Fiber: 3g

Preparation Time: 5 minutes

10. Sweet Potato and Turkey Hash

Ingredients:

- 1/2 cup sweet potato, grated
- 2 oz lean ground turkey
- 1/4 cup onion, diced
- 1/4 cup bell peppers, diced
- 1 tsp olive oil
- Salt and pepper to taste

Preparation:

1. In a pan, heat olive oil and sauté onions and bell peppers.
2. Add ground turkey and cook until browned.
3. Add grated sweet potato and cook until tender.
4. Season with salt and pepper before serving.

Servings: 1

Nutritional Value (approx.): Calories: 280, Protein: 20g, Carbohydrates: 30g, Fat: 10g, Fiber: 6g

Cooking Time: 15 minutes

11. Cherry Almond Overnight Oats

Ingredients:

- 1/2 cup rolled oats
- 1/2 cup unsweetened almond milk
- 1/4 cup fresh cherries, pitted and halved
- 1 tbsp almond butter
- 1 tsp chia seeds

Preparation:

1. In a jar, mix rolled oats, almond milk, cherries, almond butter, and chia seeds.
2. Refrigerate overnight and enjoy in the morning.

Servings: 1

Nutritional Value (approx.):

- Calories: 240
- Protein: 10g
- Carbohydrates: 30g
- Fat: 10g
- Fiber: 7g

Preparation Time: Overnight

12. Mushroom and Spinach Egg Scramble

Ingredients:

- 2 eggs
- 1/2 cup mushrooms, sliced
- 1 cup spinach leaves
- 1 tbsp olive oil
- Salt and pepper to taste

Preparation:

1. In a pan, heat olive oil and sauté mushrooms until golden.
2. Add spinach leaves and cook until wilted.
3. Whisk eggs and pour over the vegetables.
4. Scramble until eggs are cooked.
5. Season with salt and pepper before serving.

Servings: 1

Nutritional Value (approx.): Calories: 220, Protein: 15g, Carbohydrates: 5g, Fat: 16g, Fiber: 3g

Cooking Time: 10 minutes

Lunches for Lasting Strength:

13. Salmon and Quinoa Salad

Ingredients:

- 4 oz grilled salmon fillet
- 1/2 cup cooked quinoa
- 1 cup mixed salad greens
- 1/4 cup cherry tomatoes, halved
- 1/4 cup cucumber, sliced
- Lemon vinaigrette dressing

Preparation:

1. Grill salmon until cooked.
2. In a bowl, combine quinoa, salad greens, cherry tomatoes, and cucumber.
3. Top with grilled salmon.
4. Drizzle with lemon vinaigrette.

Servings: 1

Nutritional Value (approx.): Calories: 350, Protein: 25g, Carbohydrates: 30g, Fat: 15g, Fiber: 5g

Cooking Time: 15 minutes

14. Turkey and Avocado Wrap

Ingredients:

- 4 oz sliced turkey breast
- 1 whole-grain wrap
- 1/4 avocado, sliced
- 1/2 cup spinach leaves
- 1 tbsp Greek yogurt
- Mustard for taste

Preparation:

1. Lay the whole-grain wrap flat.
2. Layer turkey slices, avocado, and spinach leaves.
3. Spread Greek yogurt and mustard.
4. Roll the wrap and slice in half.

Servings: 1

Nutritional Value (approx.): Calories: 300, Protein: 20g, Carbohydrates: 25g, Fat: 12g, Fiber: 6g

Preparation Time: 10 minutes

15. Vegetarian Chickpea Stir-Fry

Ingredients:

- 1 cup chickpeas, cooked
- 1 cup broccoli florets
- 1/2 cup bell peppers, sliced
- 1/4 cup carrots, julienned
- 1 tbsp sesame oil
- Low-sodium soy sauce

Preparation:

1. Heat sesame oil in a pan.
2. Add broccoli, bell peppers, and carrots. Stir-fry until tender.
3. Add chickpeas and soy sauce. Cook for an additional 2 minutes.

Servings: 1

Nutritional Value (approx.): Calories: 280, Protein: 15g, Carbohydrates: 35g, Fat: 10g, Fiber: 10g

Cooking Time: 15 minutes

16. Mediterranean Quinoa Bowl

Ingredients:

- 1/2 cup cooked quinoa
- 2 tbsp feta cheese, crumbled
- 1/4 cup Kalamata olives, sliced
- 1/2 cup cherry tomatoes, halved
- 1/4 cup cucumber, diced
- Tzatziki sauce for dressing

Preparation:

1. In a bowl, combine quinoa, feta cheese, olives, cherry tomatoes, and cucumber.
2. Drizzle with tzatziki sauce.

Servings: 1

Nutritional Value (approx.):

- Calories: 320
- Protein: 12g
- Carbohydrates: 40g
- Fat: 14g
- Fiber: 7g

Preparation Time: 10 minutes

17. Chicken and Vegetable Skewers

Ingredients:

- 4 oz grilled chicken breast, cubed
- 1/2 cup cherry tomatoes
- 1/2 cup bell peppers, cut into chunks
- 1/4 cup red onion, sliced
- Olive oil and herbs for marinade

Preparation:

1. Marinate chicken in olive oil and herbs.
2. Skewer chicken, cherry tomatoes, bell peppers, and red onion.
3. Grill until chicken is cooked through.

Servings: 1

Nutritional Value (approx.):

- Calories: 280
- Protein: 30g
- Carbohydrates: 20g
- Fat: 10g
- Fiber: 5g

Cooking Time: 15 minutes

18. Spinach and Mushroom Quesadilla

Ingredients:

- 1 whole-grain tortilla
- 1/2 cup fresh spinach leaves
- 1/2 cup mushrooms, sliced
- 2 tbsp low-fat cheese, shredded
- Salsa for dipping

Preparation:

1. Lay the tortilla flat.
2. Layer spinach, mushrooms, and shredded cheese on one side.
3. Fold the tortilla in half and cook on a skillet until cheese melts.
4. Serve with salsa.

Servings: 1

Nutritional Value (approx.): Calories: 250, Protein: 15g, Carbohydrates: 30g, Fat: 8g, Fiber: 6g

Cooking Time: 10 minutes

19. Lentil and Vegetable Soup

Ingredients:

- 1/2 cup lentils, cooked
- 1/2 cup carrots, diced
- 1/2 cup celery, chopped
- 1/2 cup tomatoes, diced
- 1/4 cup onion, diced
- Low-sodium vegetable broth

Preparation:

1. In a pot, combine lentils, carrots, celery, tomatoes, and onion.
2. Add vegetable broth and simmer until vegetables are tender.

Servings: 1

Nutritional Value (approx.):

- Calories: 220
- Protein: 18g
- Carbohydrates: 35g
- Fat: 2g
- Fiber: 12g

Cooking Time: 20 minutes

20. Shrimp and Broccoli Stir-Fry

Ingredients:

- 4 oz shrimp, peeled and deveined
- 1 cup broccoli florets
- 1/2 cup snap peas
- 1/4 cup bell peppers, sliced
- 1 tbsp low-sodium soy sauce
- 1 tsp sesame oil

Preparation:

1. Heat sesame oil in a pan.
2. Add shrimp, broccoli, snap peas, and bell peppers. Stir-fry until shrimp is cooked.
3. Add soy sauce and toss until well combined.

Servings: 1

Nutritional Value (approx.):

- Calories: 260
- Protein: 25g
- Carbohydrates: 20g
- Fat: 8g
- Fiber: 6g

Cooking Time: 15 minutes

21. Caprese Salad with Grilled Chicken

Ingredients:

- 4 oz grilled chicken breast, sliced
- 1 cup cherry tomatoes, halved
- 1/2 cup fresh mozzarella, sliced
- Fresh basil leaves
- Balsamic glaze for drizzling

Preparation:

1. Arrange sliced grilled chicken, cherry tomatoes, and mozzarella on a plate.
2. Garnish with fresh basil leaves.
3. Drizzle with balsamic glaze.

Servings: 1

Nutritional Value (approx.):

- Calories: 280
- Protein: 30g
- Carbohydrates: 10g
- Fat: 15g
- Fiber: 2g

Preparation Time: 10 minutes

22. Egg and Veggie Wrap

Ingredients:

- 2 eggs, scrambled
- 1 whole-grain wrap
- 1/2 cup bell peppers, diced
- 1/4 cup onion, diced
- 1/4 cup spinach leaves
- Salsa for topping

Preparation:

1. Scramble eggs in a pan until cooked.
2. Lay the whole-grain wrap flat.
3. Layer scrambled eggs, bell peppers, onion, and spinach.
4. Top with salsa.

Servings: 1

Nutritional Value (approx.): Calories: 280, Protein: 18g, Carbohydrates: 30g, Fat: 12g, Fiber: 6g

Cooking Time: 10 minutes

23. Chickpea and Vegetable Curry

Ingredients:

- 1 cup chickpeas, cooked
- 1/2 cup zucchini, diced
- 1/2 cup tomatoes, diced
- 1/4 cup onion, diced
- 1 tbsp curry powder
- 1/2 cup coconut milk

Preparation:

1. In a pot, combine chickpeas, zucchini, tomatoes, onion, curry powder, and coconut milk.
2. Simmer until vegetables are tender.

Servings: 1

Nutritional Value (approx.):

- Calories: 300
- Protein: 15g
- Carbohydrates: 40g
- Fat: 12g
- Fiber: 10g

Cooking Time: 20 minutes

24. Avocado and Black Bean Salad

Ingredients:

- 1/2 cup black beans, cooked
- 1/2 avocado, diced
- 1/2 cup corn kernels
- 1/4 cup red onion, finely chopped
- Cilantro for garnish and Lime dressing

Preparation:

1. In a bowl, combine black beans, avocado, corn, and red onion.
2. Drizzle with lime dressing and garnish with cilantro.

Servings: 1

Nutritional Value (approx.):

- Calories: 250
- Protein: 10g
- Carbohydrates: 30g
- Fat: 12g
- Fiber: 10g

Preparation Time: 10 minutes

Dinner Delights for Bone Wellness:

25. Salmon and Asparagus Foil Packets

Ingredients:

- 2 salmon fillets
- 1 bunch asparagus, trimmed
- 1 lemon, sliced
- 2 tbsp olive oil
- Garlic powder, salt, and pepper to taste

Preparation:

1. Preheat the oven to 400°F (200°C).
2. Place each salmon fillet on a piece of foil.
3. Arrange asparagus around the salmon.
4. Drizzle with olive oil and season with garlic powder, salt, and pepper.
5. Seal the foil packets and bake for 20 minutes.

Servings: 2

Nutritional Value (approx.): Calories: 300, Protein: 30g, Carbohydrates: 8g, Fat: 15g, Fiber: 4g

Cooking Time: 20 minutes

26. Quinoa-Stuffed Bell Peppers

Ingredients:

- 2 bell peppers, halved and seeds removed
- 1 cup cooked quinoa
- 1/2 cup black beans, drained and rinsed
- 1/2 cup corn kernels
- 1/2 cup diced tomatoes
- 1/4 cup shredded cheese
- Cumin, chili powder, salt, and pepper to taste

Preparation:

1. Preheat the oven to 375°F (190°C).
2. In a bowl, mix quinoa, black beans, corn, tomatoes, and spices.
3. Stuff bell peppers with the quinoa mixture.
4. Top with shredded cheese and bake for 25 minutes.

Servings: 2

Nutritional Value (approx.): Calories: 320, Protein: 15g, Carbohydrates: 45g, Fat: 10g, Fiber: 9g

Cooking Time: 25 minutes

27. Baked Chicken with Lemon and Rosemary

Ingredients:

- 2 chicken breasts
- 1 lemon, juiced and zested
- 2 tbsp olive oil
- 2 cloves garlic, minced
- Fresh rosemary, chopped
- Salt and pepper to taste

Preparation:

1. Preheat the oven to 375°F (190°C).
2. In a bowl, mix lemon juice, lemon zest, olive oil, garlic, rosemary, salt, and pepper.
3. Coat chicken breasts with the mixture and bake for 30 minutes.

Servings: 2

Nutritional Value (approx.): Calories: 280, Protein: 30g, Carbohydrates: 2g, Fat: 15g, Fiber: 1g

Cooking Time: 30 minutes

28. Vegetarian Stir-Fry with Tofu

Ingredients:

- 1 cup firm tofu, cubed
- 1 cup broccoli florets
- 1 bell pepper, sliced
- 1 carrot, julienned
- 2 tbsp soy sauce
- 1 tbsp sesame oil
- 1 tsp ginger, minced
- Brown rice for serving

Preparation:

1. In a wok, sauté tofu until golden.
2. Add broccoli, bell pepper, carrot, soy sauce, sesame oil, and ginger.
3. Stir-fry until vegetables are tender.
4. Serve over brown rice.

Servings: 2

Nutritional Value (approx.): Calories: 320, Protein: 18g, Carbohydrates: 30g, Fat: 15g, Fiber: 6g

Cooking Time: 15 minutes

29. Mushroom and Spinach Stuffed Chicken Breast

Ingredients:

- 2 chicken breasts
- 1 cup mushrooms, chopped
- 1 cup fresh spinach
- 1/4 cup feta cheese, crumbled
- 1 tsp olive oil
- Garlic powder, salt, and pepper to taste

Preparation:

1. Preheat the oven to 375°F (190°C).
2. In a pan, sauté mushrooms and spinach in olive oil until wilted.
3. Butterfly chicken breasts and stuff with the mushroom and spinach mixture.
4. Sprinkle feta cheese on top and bake for 25 minutes.

Servings: 2

Nutritional Value (approx.): Calories: 280, Protein: 30g, Carbohydrates: 4g, Fat: 15g, Fiber: 2g

Cooking Time: 25 minutes

30. Lemon Garlic Shrimp and Zucchini Noodles

Ingredients:

- 8 oz shrimp, peeled and deveined
- 2 zucchinis, spiralized
- 2 tbsp olive oil
- 2 cloves garlic, minced
- 1 lemon, juiced and zested
- Fresh parsley for garnish
- Salt and pepper to taste

Preparation:

1. In a pan, sauté shrimp in olive oil until pink.
2. Add garlic, lemon juice, and zucchini noodles.
3. Cook until noodles are tender.
4. Garnish with lemon zest and fresh parsley.

Servings: 2

Nutritional Value (approx.): Calories: 250, Protein: 25g, Carbohydrates: 10g, Fat: 12g, Fiber: 4g

Cooking Time: 15 minutes

31. Spinach and Feta Stuffed Portobello Mushrooms

Ingredients:

- 4 large portobello mushrooms
- 2 cups fresh spinach
- 1/2 cup feta cheese, crumbled
- 2 tbsp balsamic vinegar
- 1 tbsp olive oil
- Garlic powder, salt, and pepper to taste

Preparation:

1. Preheat the oven to 375°F (190°C).
2. Remove the stems from portobello mushrooms.
3. In a pan, sauté spinach in olive oil until wilted.
4. Stuff mushrooms with spinach and feta.
5. Drizzle with balsamic vinegar and bake for 20 minutes.

Servings: 2

Nutritional Value (approx.): Calories: 220, Protein: 15g, Carbohydrates: 15g, Fat: 12g, Fiber: 5g

Cooking Time: 20 minutes

32. Turkey and Vegetable Skewers

Ingredients:

- 1 lb turkey breast, cut into cubes
- 1 zucchini, sliced
- 1 bell pepper, diced
- Cherry tomatoes
- 2 tbsp olive oil
- Lemon zest and juice
- Italian seasoning, salt, and pepper to taste

Preparation:

1. Preheat the grill or grill pan.
2. In a bowl, mix turkey cubes, zucchini, bell pepper, and cherry tomatoes.
3. Thread onto skewers.
4. In a separate bowl, mix olive oil, lemon zest, lemon juice, Italian seasoning, salt, and pepper.
5. Brush the skewers with the mixture and grill for 15 minutes.

Servings: 2

Nutritional Value (approx.): Calories: 300, Protein: 30g, Carbohydrates: 10g, Fat: 15g, Fiber: 3g

Cooking Time: 15 minutes

33. Eggplant and Tomato Bake

Ingredients:

- 1 large eggplant, sliced
- 2 large tomatoes, sliced
- 1/2 cup mozzarella cheese, shredded
- 2 tbsp olive oil
- Fresh basil for garnish
- Garlic powder, salt, and pepper to taste

Preparation:

1. Preheat the oven to 375°F (190°C).
2. In a baking dish, layer eggplant and tomato slices.
3. Drizzle with olive oil and season with garlic powder, salt, and pepper.
4. Top with mozzarella cheese and bake for 30 minutes.

Servings: 2

Nutritional Value (approx.): Calories: 250, Protein: 10g, Carbohydrates: 15g, Fat: 18g, Fiber: 8g

Cooking Time: 30 minutes

34. Chickpea and Spinach Curry

Ingredients:

- 1 can chickpeas, drained and rinsed
- 2 cups fresh spinach
- 1 onion, finely chopped
- 2 tomatoes, diced
- 1/2 cup coconut milk
- 2 tbsp curry powder
- 1 tbsp olive oil
- Cilantro for garnish
- Salt and pepper to taste

Preparation:

1. In a pan, sauté onion in olive oil until translucent.
2. Add tomatoes, chickpeas, curry powder, and coconut milk.
3. Simmer for 15 minutes.
4. Stir in fresh spinach and cook until wilted.
5. Garnish with cilantro before serving.

Servings: 2

Nutritional Value (approx.): Calories: 280, Protein: 12g, Carbohydrates: 30g, Fat: 14g, Fiber: 8g

Cooking Time: 20 minutes

---

35. Pesto Zoodles with Cherry Tomatoes

Ingredients:

- 2 zucchinis, spiralized
- 1 cup cherry tomatoes, halved
- 1/4 cup pesto sauce
- 2 tbsp Parmesan cheese, grated
- Pine nuts for garnish

Preparation:

1. In a pan, sauté zoodles until tender.
2. Add cherry tomatoes and cook for an additional 2 minutes.
3. Toss with pesto sauce.
4. Garnish with Parmesan cheese and pine nuts.

Servings: 2

Nutritional Value (approx.): Calories: 260, Protein: 8g, Carbohydrates: 15g, Fat: 20g, Fiber: 4g

Cooking Time: 10 minutes

36. Lentil and Vegetable Soup

Ingredients:

- 1 cup dried lentils, rinsed
- 1 onion, chopped
- 2 carrots, diced
- 2 celery stalks, sliced
- 3 cloves garlic, minced
- 6 cups vegetable broth
- 1 can diced tomatoes
- 1 tsp cumin
- 1 tsp paprika
- Salt and pepper to taste

Preparation:

1. In a pot, sauté onion, carrots, celery, and garlic until softened.
2. Add lentils, vegetable broth, diced tomatoes, cumin, paprika, salt, and pepper.
3. Simmer for 30 minutes.

Servings: 4

Nutritional Value (approx.):

- Calories: 280
- Protein: 18g
- Carbohydrates: 45g
- Fat: 2g
- Fiber: 15g

Cooking Time: 30 minutes

CONCLUSION

As we bring the curtain down on the "Osteoporosis Diet Cookbook for Women," it's a moment of reflection—a journey we've navigated together toward fortifying your bones, elevating bone health, and embracing a vibrant, nourishing lifestyle. Throughout these pages, we've ventured into a world of delectable and nutrient-rich recipes intricately crafted to support women confronting the hurdles of osteoporosis.

This cookbook transcends its role as a mere collection of recipes; it's a guide, an instrument empowering you to seize control of your bone health through the choices you make in the kitchen. We've delved into the science underpinning osteoporosis, unraveling its complexities and deciphering the nutritional elements that can be instrumental in managing, and even reversing, its effects. From dawn's breakfast to the evening's dinner and the snacks in between, each recipe stands as a fusion of flavor and nutrition, meticulously designed to supply the essential nutrients your bones yearn for.

In embarking on this culinary odyssey, remember that the echoes of your choices extend far beyond the kitchen's aromatic delights and taste bud revelations.

They resonate through your body, fortifying your bones, nurturing your well-being, and shaping the trajectory of your overall health journey.

This cookbook stands as a testament to the notion that food is more than sustenance—it's a potent ally in the pursuit of a healthier, stronger version of yourself.

This isn't merely about adopting a diet; it's about embracing a lifestyle—a lifestyle that places your bone health at the forefront, radiates vitality, and revels in the joy of intentionally nourishing your body. The recipes within these pages aren't constraints; they're an invitation to relish the abundance of nature, discovering the harmonious blend of flavors that contribute to your well-being.

As you turn the final page, carry the lessons gleaned here into your daily life. Let this cookbook be the catalyst for a transformative journey—one where you approach food with mindfulness, savoring the knowledge that every bite propels you toward stronger bones and a healthier you.

Dear reader, your odyssey toward optimal bone health commences now. Let this cookbook be your unwavering companion, directing you toward a life replete with delightful, nutritious meals that not only tantalize your taste buds but also fortify your bones.

Your health is a voyage, and with each recipe, you stride toward a future where your bones are unyielding, and your body thrives.

Embrace the potency of this osteoporosis diet; let it be the cornerstone of a life infused with strength, vitality, and the joy of nourishing yourself from within.

Cheers to your journey and to the vibrant, bone-healthy life awaiting you!

DATE: ____________

	BREAKFAST	LUNCH	DINNER	SHOPPING LIST
MON				
TUES				
WED				
THURS				
FRI				
SAT				
SUN				

MEAL PLANNER

DATE:

	BREAKFAST	LUNCH	DINNER	SHOPPING LIST
MON				
TUES				
WED				
THURS				
FRI				
SAT				
SUN				

MEAL PLANNER

DATE:

	BREAKFAST	LUNCH	DINNER	SHOPPING LIST
MON				
TUES				
WED				
THURS				
FRI				
SAT				
SUN				

MEAL PLANNER

DATE:

	BREAKFAST	LUNCH	DINNER	SHOPPING LIST
MON				
TUES				
WED				
THURS				
FRI				
SAT				
SUN				

MEAL PLANNER

DATE: ____________

	BREAKFAST	LUNCH	DINNER	SHOPPING LIST
MON				
TUES				
WED				
THURS				
FRI				
SAT				
SUN				

MEAL PLANNER

DATE:

	BREAKFAST	LUNCH	DINNER	SHOPPING LIST
MON				
TUES				
WED				
THURS				
FRI				
SAT				
SUN				

MEAL PLANNER

DATE: ____________

	BREAKFAST	LUNCH	DINNER	SHOPPING LIST
MON				
TUES				
WED				
THURS				
FRI				
SAT				
SUN				

MEAL PLANNER

DATE: ______

	BREAKFAST	LUNCH	DINNER	SHOPPING LIST
MON				
TUES				
WED				
THURS				
FRI				
SAT				
SUN				

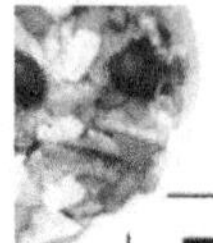

	BREAKFAST	LUNCH	DINNER	SHOPPING LIST
MON				
TUES				
WED				
THURS				
FRI				
SAT				
SUN				

MEAL PLANNER

DATE: ______

	BREAKFAST	LUNCH	DINNER	SHOPPING LIST
MON				
TUES				
WED				
THURS				
FRI				
SAT				
SUN				

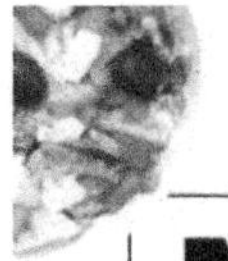

MEAL PLANNER

DATE: ____________

	BREAKFAST	LUNCH	DINNER	SHOPPING LIST
MON				
TUES				
WED				
THURS				
FRI				
SAT				
SUN				

MEAL PLANNER

DATE: ______

	BREAKFAST	LUNCH	DINNER	SHOPPING LIST
MON				
TUES				
WED				
THURS				
FRI				
SAT				
SUN				

MEAL PLANNER

DATE: ____________________

	BREAKFAST	LUNCH	DINNER	SHOPPING LIST
MON				
TUES				
WED				
THURS				
FRI				
SAT				
SUN				

Made in the USA
Las Vegas, NV
10 December 2024